2016

JANUARY

M	T	W	T	F	S	S
				1	2	3
4	5	6	7	8	9	10
11	12	13	14	15	16	17
18	19	20	21	22	23	24
25	26	27	28	29	30	31

FEBRUARY

M	T	W	T	F	S	S
1	2	3	4	5	6	7
8	9	10	11	12	13	14
15	16	17	18	19	20	21
22	23	24	25	26	27	28
29						

MARCH

M	T	W	T	F	S	S
	1	2	3	4	5	6
7	8	9	10	11	12	13
14	15	16	17	18	19	20
21	22	23	24	25	26	27
28	29	30	31			

APRIL

M	T	W	T	F	S	S
				1	2	3
4	5	6	7	8	9	10
11	12	13	14	15	16	17
18	19	20	21	22	23	24
25	26	27	28	29	30	

MAY

M	T	W	T	F	S	S
						1
2	3	4	5	6	7	8
9	10	11	12	13	14	15
16	17	18	19	20	21	22
23	24	25	26	27	28	29
30	31					

JUNE

M	T	W	T	F	S	S
		1	2	3	4	5
6	7	8	9	10	11	12
13	14	15	16	17	18	19
20	21	22	23	24	25	26
27	28	29	30			

JULY

M	T	W	T	F	S	S
				1	2	3
4	5	6	7	8	9	10
11	12	13	14	15	16	17
18	19	20	21	22	23	24
25	26	27	28	29	30	31

AUGUST

M	T	W	T	F	S	S
1	2	3	4	5	6	7
8	9	10	11	12	13	14
15	16	17	18	19	20	21
22	23	24	25	26	27	28
29	30	31				

SEPTEMBER

M	T	W	T	F	S	S
			1	2	3	4
5	6	7	8	9	10	11
12	13	14	15	16	17	18
19	20	21	22	23	24	25
26	27	28	29	30		

OCTOBER

M	T	W	T	F	S	S
					1	2
3	4	5	6	7	8	9
10	11	12	13	14	15	16
17	18	19	20	21	22	23
24	25	26	27	28	29	30
31						

NOVEMBER

M	T	W	T	F	S	S
	1	2	3	4	5	6
7	8	9	10	11	12	13
14	15	16	17	18	19	20
21	22	23	24	25	26	27
28	29	30				

DECEMBER

M	T	W	T	F	S	S
			1	2	3	4
5	6	7	8	9	10	11
12	13	14	15	16	17	18
19	20	21	22	23	24	25
26	27	28	29	30	31	

PERSONAL INFORMATION

NAME: Jessica Streeter-Smith

ADDRESS: 22 Castlehill park, Inverness, IU25GJ

HOME TEL: 01463 790078

MOBILE:

EMAIL: a.streetersmith@btinternet.com

IN CASE OF EMERGENCY PLEASE CONTACT:

NAME: Jessica Streeter-Smith

ADDRESS: 22 Castlehill park

HOME TEL: 01463 790078

MOBILE:

EMAIL: a.streetersmith@btinternet.com

DOCTOR: ?

BLOOD GROUP: ?

ALLERGIES: Penicilon

NATIONAL INSURANCE N°: ?

CAR REGISTRATION N°: ?

PASSPORT N°: ?

CONVERSIONS

WEIGHT

METRIC	IMPERIAL
50g	2oz
75g	2½oz
100g	4oz
125g	4½oz
150g	5oz
175g	6oz
200g	7oz
225g	8oz
250g	9oz
300g	11oz
350g	12oz
400g	14oz
450g	1lb
500g	1lb 2oz
550g	1lb 4oz
600g	1lb 5oz
650g	1lb 7oz
700g	1lb 9oz
750g	1lb 10oz
800g	1lb 12oz
850g	1lb 14oz
900g	2lb
950g	2lb 2oz
1kg	2lb 4oz

VOLUME

METRIC	IMPERIAL
30ml	1fl oz
50ml	2fl oz
75ml	2½fl oz
100ml	3½fl oz
125ml	4fl oz
150ml	¼ pint
175ml	6fl oz
200ml	7fl oz
225ml	8fl oz
250ml	9fl oz
300ml	½ pint
350ml	12fl oz
400ml	14fl oz
425ml	¾ pint
450ml	16fl oz
500ml	18fl oz
600ml	1 pint
700ml	1¼ pint
850ml	1½ pint
1 litre	1¾ pint

SPOON MEASURES

METRIC	IMPERIAL
5ml	1tsp
10ml	2tsp
15ml	1tbsp
30ml	2tbsp
45ml	3tbsp
60ml	4tbsp
75ml	5tbsp

TEMPERATURE

GAS MARK	°F	°C
¼	250	120
1	275	140
2	300	150
3	325	160
4	350	180
5	375	190
6	400	200
7	425	220
8	450	230
9	475	240

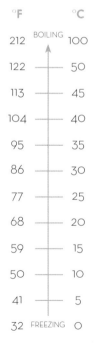

°F		°C
212	BOILING	100
122		50
113		45
104		40
95		35
86		30
77		25
68		20
59		15
50		10
41		5
32	FREEZING	0

NOTES

SPECIAL DATES

JANUARY

Mary's birthday

FEBRUARY

MARCH

Mum's birthday
Abigais birthday

APRIL

My birthday
Rosies birthday

MAY

Dad,Harry,Evies birthday

JUNE

JULY

AUGUST

Emilys birthday

SEPTEMBER

OCTOBER

NOVEMBER

DECEMBER

DEC 2015/JAN 2016

28   MONDAY

29   TUESDAY

30   WEDNESDAY

31   THURSDAY

1   FRIDAY

New Year's Holiday (UK & Republic of Ireland)

2   SATURDAY

3   SUNDAY

PECAN SHORTIES

The best shortbread is made to the classic recipe of one part sugar to two of butter and three of flour. Icing sugar gives a crisper texture than caster sugar (which makes them sandy and crumbly or 'short'). Toasted nuts and melted chocolate make these shorties extra special.

JANUARY

4	MONDAY

5	TUESDAY

6	WEDNESDAY

Ava's birthday

7	THURSDAY

8	FRIDAY

9	SATURDAY

Marys birthday

10	SUNDAY

PECAN SHORTIES

75g pecan halves
250g plain flour
175g unsalted butter, softened
85g icing sugar, sifted
½ teaspoon vanilla extract

To finish
100g dark chocolate (about 70% cocoa solids), chopped

You will also need
2 baking sheets, lined with baking paper

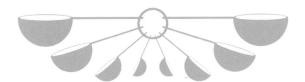

JANUARY

11   MONDAY

12   TUESDAY

13   WEDNESDAY

14   THURSDAY

15   FRIDAY

16   SATURDAY

17   SUNDAY

PECAN SHORTIES

1 Heat your oven to 180°C/350°F/gas 4. Tip the nuts into a small tin and toast in the heated oven for 5–7 minutes until lightly coloured. Leave to cool, then chop or break up the nuts fairly coarsely. Mix with the flour in a bowl. Set aside.

2 Put the soft butter into another mixing bowl (or the bowl of a free-standing electric mixer fitted with the whisk attachment). Beat with a wooden spoon (or the mixer) until the butter is as smooth and creamy as mayonnaise.

3 Beat in the icing sugar a tablespoon at a time (use the lowest speed of the mixer). Once all the sugar has been worked in, add the vanilla and beat well for a couple of minutes until the mixture becomes almost white in colour and light and fluffy in texture (about a minute in the mixer). Add the flour and nut mixture and stir in with a wooden spoon or plastic spatula to make a firm dough.

4 Divide the dough into 20 even-sized pieces. Lightly flour your hands and roll each piece into a neat ball. Set the balls on the lined baking sheets, spacing them well apart to allow for spreading. Gently squash each ball with your fingers to make a disc about 5.5cm across and 1cm thick.

5 Bake in the heated oven for 14–16 minutes until pale gold in colour with slightly darker edges, rotating the baking sheets halfway through so the shortbreads bake evenly. Set the sheets on a heatproof surface. Leave the shortbreads to firm up for 5 minutes before transferring them to a wire rack to cool completely. Leave the lined sheets on the worktop.

6 Once the biscuits are cold, gently melt the chocolate in a heatproof bowl set over a pan of steaming hot water. Remove the bowl from the pan and stir the chocolate until smooth.

7 Hold one shortbread horizontally by the sides and gently dip the base into the melted chocolate so that the chocolate comes halfway up the sides of the biscuit. Lay the shortie chocolate side up on a lined baking sheet. Repeat with the rest of the shorties, then leave to set. Once the chocolate is firm and hard, store in an airtight container for about 3 days.

MAKES TWENTY

JANUARY

18 MONDAY

19 TUESDAY

20 WEDNESDAY

21 THURSDAY

Lisa's birthday

22 FRIDAY

23 SATURDAY

24 SUNDAY

NOTES

For my birthday I really
would like a trampoline

JANUARY

25   MONDAY

26   TUESDAY

27   WEDNESDAY

28   THURSDAY

29   FRIDAY

30   SATURDAY

31   SUNDAY

FEBRUARY

| 1 | MONDAY |

| 2 | TUESDAY |

| 3 | WEDNESDAY |

| 4 | THURSDAY |

| 5 | FRIDAY |

| 6 | SATURDAY |

| 7 | SUNDAY |

Gymnastics
Competititon

SNOWBALL MERINGUES

Fluffy, snowy-white balls of meringue covered in whipped cream and then in white chocolate – a bit of fun to make and eat! You can experiment with different chocolate, or use finely chopped nuts or desiccated coconut (try tinting the coconut with a few drops of food colouring; leave to dry before using).

FEBRUARY

8   MONDAY

Chinese New Year

9   TUESDAY

10   WEDNESDAY

Ash Wednesday

11   THURSDAY

12   FRIDAY

13   SATURDAY

14   SUNDAY

St. Valentine's Day

SNOWBALL MERINGUES

For the meringue
3 medium free-range egg whites, at room temperature
good pinch of cream of tartar
90g caster sugar (white, not golden)
90g icing sugar (white, not golden)

To decorate
250ml whipping cream, well chilled
1 ½ tablespoons icing sugar
½ teaspoon vanilla extract
85g good-quality white chocolate, grated, OR 50g unsweetened
desiccated coconut OR finely chopped almonds

You will also need
2 baking sheets, lined with baking paper
pretty paper or foil cupcake cases

FEBRUARY

15 MONDAY

16 TUESDAY

17 WEDNESDAY

18 THURSDAY

19 FRIDAY

20 SATURDAY

21 SUNDAY

SNOWBALL MERINGUES

1 Heat your oven to 110°C/225°F/gas ¼. Put the egg whites into a large, clean and grease-free mixing bowl (or the bowl of a free-standing electric mixer fitted with the whisk attachment). Add the cream of tartar – this helps to build and strengthen the structure of the meringue – then start to whisk with a hand-held electric mixer (or using slow speed in the freestanding mixer).

2 Once the whites look frothy – this barely takes a minute – increase the speed and whisk until the mixture is fairly thick and frothy (but not yet at 'soft peak' stage). Whisk in a third of the caster sugar, a tablespoon at a time, and continue whisking just until the mixture will form soft, slightly floppy peaks when the whisk is lifted from the bowl. Whisk in half the remaining caster sugar in the same way, then whisk until the mixture will form stiff peaks. Quickly whisk in the rest of the caster sugar and carry on whisking for exactly 1 minute to make a very stiff and glossy meringue. Set a sieve over the bowl and sift the icing sugar on to the meringue, then carefully but thoroughly fold in with a large metal spoon or plastic spatula.

3 Shape the meringue into balls about 5.5cm across: to make each one, scoop up some meringue with a soup spoon and use a second spoon to push the ball of meringue gently onto the lined baking sheet. If necessary, carefully tidy up and smooth the ball shape with a palette knife, but don't fiddle too much as the meringue will eventually be covered with cream. Set the meringues slightly apart on the lined baking sheet to allow for expansion.

4 Bake in the heated oven for about 3 hours until crisp and dry, but still very pale. Turn off the oven and leave the meringues in the cooling oven to finish drying. Once cold, they can be stored in an airtight container for up to 5 days before decorating.

5 When you are ready to finish the snowballs, pour the cream into a chilled bowl, add the icing sugar and vanilla, and whip until the cream is very thick.

MAKES ABOUT FIVE

FEBRUARY

22 MONDAY

23 TUESDAY

24 WEDNESDAY

25 THURSDAY

26 FRIDAY

27 SATURDAY

28 SUNDAY

NOTES

Make Sure I take out
the bins

FEBRUARY/MARCH

29   MONDAY

1   TUESDAY

St. David's Day (Wales)
2   WEDNESDAY

3   THURSDAY

4   FRIDAY

5   SATURDAY

6   SUNDAY

Mothering Sunday (UK)

CHOCOLATE PECAN MACARONS

The finest of French macarons are made with almonds ground almost to a powder. These macarons, which use ground pecans and plenty of cocoa, may not look quite so chic but they have the most wonderful flavour that becomes more intense as the macarons age. The filling is a contrast of creamy white and bitter chocolate ganaches. For a very glam finish, lightly dust the sandwiched macarons with edible gold dust.

MARCH

7 MONDAY

8 TUESDAY

9 WEDNESDAY

10 THURSDAY

11 FRIDAY

12 SATURDAY

13 SUNDAY

CHOCOLATE PECAN MACARONS

For the macarons
100g pecans
75g icing sugar
2 large free-range egg whites, at room temperature
good pinch of salt
75g caster sugar
25g cocoa powder

For the ganaches
50g good-quality white chocolate, finely chopped
50g dark chocolate (about 70% cocoa solids), finely chopped
100ml whipping cream

You will also need
1 baking sheet, lined with baking paper
piping bag
1.5cm plain tube
a star tube (OR a duo piping bag fitted with the star tube)

MARCH

14   MONDAY

15   TUESDAY

16   WEDNESDAY

17   THURSDAY

St. Patrick's Day Holiday (Ireland)

18   FRIDAY

19   SATURDAY

20   SUNDAY

CHOCOLATE PECAN MACARONS

1 Draw 18 x 5cm circles on the sheet of baking paper (use a 5cm cutter as a guide), then turn the paper over and lay it on the baking sheet. Tip the pecans and icing sugar into the bowl of a food processor and grind to a fine, sandy powder. Set aside for now.

2 Put the egg whites and salt into a spotlessly clean and grease-free mixing bowl, or the bowl of a free-standing electric mixer. Whisk until the whites stand in soft peaks that slightly flop at the tip when you lift out the whisk.

3 Whisk in the caster sugar a tablespoon at a time, on full speed, then continue to whisk until the mixture stands in stiff peaks (no flopping) when the whisk is lifted.

4 Sift the cocoa powder into the bowl and add the pecan mixture. Gently but thoroughly fold everything together with a large metal spoon or plastic spatula until there are no streaks: the mixture will feel slightly stiffer than the usual almond macaron mixture.

5 Transfer the mixture to the piping bag fitted with the plain tube. Pipe small mounds of the mixture just inside each circle drawn on the baking paper (you can also use a teaspoon of mixture to make each macaron). Dip your finger in cold water, then gently flatten the peaks. Bang the sheet on the worktop to knock out any air pockets. Leave the macarons, on the sheet on the worktop, for 30 minutes to allow a skin to form (the macarons will look slightly matt). Meanwhile, heat your oven to 180°C/350°F/gas 4.

6 Bake in the heated oven for 15–20 minutes until the macarons feel firm when gently pressed on top – the inside centre will still be soft. Don't overcook the macarons as they will firm up as they cool and you want the centres to remain slightly soft. Carefully slide the macarons, on the sheet of baking paper, on to a wire rack and leave to cool.

7 Meanwhile, make up the 2 ganaches. Put the white chocolate into a heatproof bowl and the dark chocolate into another heatproof bowl. Heat the cream in a small saucepan until steaming hot but not quite boiling, then pour half over each type of chocolate. Leave for a minute before stirring each gently until smooth and creamy. Leave until thick and firm enough to pipe.

8 Spoon the white ganache into the washed and dried piping bag fitted with the star tube. Pipe a ring of ganache onto the flat underside of half of the macarons, leaving the middle empty. Spoon or pipe (using the cleaned piping bag fitted with the plain tube) the dark ganache into the centre of each ring. If you are using a duo piping bag fit the star tube, spoon one ganache into each side of the bag (be sure they are both the same consistency – if one is too firm, it won't work), then pipe a dual swirl to cover the flat underside of half the macarons.

9 Sandwich with the remaining macarons (flat side to flat side) to make pairs. Store in an airtight container in a cool spot (not the fridge) and eat within 4 days.

MAKES NINE PAIRS

MARCH

21 Mums birthday
Abigails birthday

MONDAY

22

TUESDAY

23

WEDNESDAY

24

THURSDAY

25

FRIDAY

Good Friday (UK)

26

SATURDAY

27

SUNDAY

Easter Sunday / Daylight Saving Begins

NOTES

MARCH/APRIL

28 MONDAY

Easter Monday (UK & Republic of Ireland)

29 TUESDAY

30 WEDNESDAY

31 THURSDAY

1 FRIDAY

April fools day
Cicilys birthday

2 SATURDAY

3 SUNDAY

MINI SPICED APPLE DOUGHNUTS

These delicious little bites are filled with a lovely spiced apple filling, but you could use cherry or raspberry jam if you prefer a more classic version.

APRIL

4 MONDAY

5 TUESDAY

6 WEDNESDAY

7 THURSDAY

8 FRIDAY

My birthday

9 SATURDAY

10 SUNDAY

MINI SPICED APPLE DOUGHNUTS

200g strong white bread flour, plus extra for dusting

a pinch of salt

50g cold unsalted butter, diced

1 x 7g sachet fast-action dried yeast

2 tablespoons caster sugar, plus extra to sprinkle

1 medium egg, beaten

80ml lukewarm full-fat milk

sunflower oil, for deep-frying and greasing

For the apple filling

2 Bramley apples, peeled, cored and chopped into small pieces

2 Cox apples, peeled, cored and chopped into small pieces

3 tablespoons caster sugar

1 cinnamon stick

4 cloves

½ teaspoon ground ginger

1 vanilla pod, slit in half lengthways

a good splash of brandy

You will also need

piping bag, fitted with a medium plain nozzle

APRIL

11 Rosies birthday MONDAY

12 TUESDAY

13 WEDNESDAY

14 THURSDAY

15 FRIDAY

16 SATURDAY

17 SUNDAY

MINI SPICED APPLE DOUGHNUTS

1 Put the flour and salt into a large bowl, then rub in the butter with your fingertips until the mixture resembles coarse crumbs. Stir through the yeast and sugar, then make a well in the centre. Mix the egg with the milk and pour into the well. Mix quickly until it comes together into a soft dough.

2 Knead the dough on a lightly floured surface for 5 minutes until smooth and supple. Lightly oil a clean bowl and place the dough in it. Cover with a clean tea towel and leave in a warm place for 1 hour or until doubled in size.

3 Meanwhile, place all the filling ingredients in a pan with a splash of water and cook gently over a low heat, stirring, until the apples are soft. Remove the aromatics and whizz to a purée in a food processor or blender. Set aside to cool.

4 Line a baking sheet with greaseproof paper. Knock back the dough and divide into 12 evenly sized pieces, then roll each into a smooth ball. Place spaced well apart on the baking tray and loosely cover with a sheet of lightly oiled clingfilm. Leave for 45 minutes in a warm place or until doubled in size again.

5 Heat the sunflower oil in a large, deep pan, no more than one-third full, to 170°C (a cube of bread will brown in about 30 seconds). Cook the doughnuts in batches of 2 or 3, frying for 30 seconds–1 minute on each side until golden and cooked through. Remove with a slotted spoon and drain on kitchen paper.

6 While the doughnuts are still warm, spoon the filling into a piping bag fitted with a medium plain nozzle or into a squeezy bottle with a nozzle end. Make a little slit in the side of each doughnut with the tip of a small, sharp knife, then squeeze some of the apple purée into the centre. Roll the filled doughnuts gently in caster sugar to coat completely, or dust well using a dredger. Serve warm or allow to cool.

MAKES TWELVE

APRIL

18 MONDAY

19 TUESDAY

20 WEDNESDAY

21 THURSDAY

22 FRIDAY

23 Black isle Cycle challenge SATURDAY

St. George's Day (England) / Passover (Pesach)

24 Miss walkers Birthday SUNDAY

Remeber Josh's birthday present

APRIL/MAY

25 Graces birthday
Georginas birthday
MONDAY

26
TUESDAY

27
WEDNESDAY

28
THURSDAY

29
FRIDAY

30
SATURDAY

1
SUNDAY

STICKY HONEY CINNAMON BUNS

If you are a fan of Chelsea Buns try these. A well-flavoured honey is essential.
You can replace the walnuts with almonds, pecans or macadamias.

MAY

2 MONDAY

May Day Holiday (UK & Republic of Ireland)

3 TUESDAY

Joshs birthday

4 WEDNESDAY

5 THURSDAY

6 FRIDAY

7 SATURDAY

Gymfest 2016 perth

8 SUNDAY

STICKY HONEY CINNAMON BUNS

For the sweet dough
450g strong white bread flour
1 x 7g sachet fast-action dried yeast
7g sea salt, crushed
1 medium free-range egg, at room temperature
2 tablespoons set honey
about 250ml lukewarm milk

For the sticky filling and topping
140g set honey
140g unsalted butter, softened
1 tablespoon ground cinnamon
140g light brown muscovado sugar
about 50ml whipping or single cream
100g walnut pieces

You will also need
1 roasting tin OR baking tin (not loose-based),
about 22 x 30 x 5cm, greased with butter

MAY

9 MONDAY

10 TUESDAY

11 WEDNESDAY

12 THURSDAY

13 FRIDAY

Dads Birthday

14 SATURDAY

Gymfest 2016 perth

15 SUNDAY

STICKY HONEY CINNAMON BUNS

1 To make the dough, put the flour, yeast and salt into a large mixing bowl (or the bowl of a free-standing electric mixer fitted with the dough hook) and mix together. Make a well in the centre.

2 Mix the egg with the honey and 225ml of the lukewarm milk. When thoroughly combined pour into the well in the flour and mix everything together by hand (or with the mixer on the lowest speed) to make a very soft but not sticky dough that leaves the side of the bowl clean – add more milk as needed to make a dough that isn't hard or dry.

3 Turn out the dough on to a lightly floured worktop and knead thoroughly for 10 minutes (or 5 minutes in the mixer on lowest speed) until the dough feels silky smooth and very stretchy.

4 Return the dough to the bowl and cover with a snap-on lid or clingfilm. Leave to rise at normal room temperature for about 1½ hours until doubled in size.

5 Punch down the risen dough to deflate it before turning it out on to a lightly floured worktop. Press or roll it out to a 25 x 30cm rectangle of even thickness. Cover lightly with a sheet of clingfilm and leave to rest while you make the filling/topping mix.

6 Put the honey, soft butter, cinnamon and sugar into a mixing bowl and beat well with a wooden spoon until smooth and slightly fluffy. Stir in just enough cream to make the mixture slightly sloppy (don't worry if it looks as if it is about to curdle).

7 Uncover the dough and spread over about a third of the cinnamon mixture. Scatter half the nuts evenly over the

dough, then roll up from one long side – the roll will feel (and look) a bit sticky at this point. Pinch the seam so the dough roll doesn't unravel, then cut across into 12 even-sized pieces with a very sharp knife.

MAKES TWELVE

8 Spoon the rest of the sticky cinnamon mixture into the prepared tin and spread evenly. Set the rolls cut side up on top, so they are barely touching. Slip the tin into a large plastic bag, slightly inflate it so the plastic won't stick to the dough as it rises and secure the ends. Leave to rise as before for about 45 minutes until doubled in size. Towards the end of the rising time, heat your oven to 180°C/350°F/gas 4.

9 Uncover the tin and bake in the heated oven for about 25 minutes until the buns are golden and the filling is bubbling up around them. Set the tin on a heatproof surface and leave to cool for a couple of minutes until the bubbling subsides.

10 Carefully run a round-bladed knife around the inside of the tin to loosen the buns. Place an upturned large rimmed baking sheet on top of the tin and very carefully turn them over while holding them tightly together – the caramel is still very hot. The buns will fall out on to the baking sheet. Lift off the tin and scrape any caramel left in the tin onto the buns.

11 Scatter the remaining nuts over the top, then leave the buns to cool before pulling them apart. These are best eaten the same or the next day.

MAY

16	MONDAY
17	TUESDAY
18	WEDNESDAY
19	THURSDAY
20	FRIDAY
21	SATURDAY
22	SUNDAY

22 Harrys Birthday
Evies birthday

NOTES

MAY

23   MONDAY

24   TUESDAY

25   WEDNESDAY

26   THURSDAY

27   FRIDAY

28   SATURDAY

29   SUNDAY

NOTES

MAY/JUNE

30 MONDAY

31 TUESDAY

1 Orienteering competition WEDNESDAY

2 THURSDAY

3 FRIDAY

4 SATURDAY

5 SUNDAY

GINGER & PEAR PUDDING

Here's a new, dramatic-looking twist on an old favourite – whole pears, stuffed with walnuts, baked upright in a dark ginger sponge pudding. The sponge is made by the melting method, like gingerbread, and quickly mixed. Choose just-ripe pears that are short and squat (rather than tall and thin) for the best results. The walnuts can be replaced with chopped stem ginger if you like.

JUNE

6   MONDAY

7   TUESDAY

8   WEDNESDAY

9   THURSDAY

10   FRIDAY

11   SATURDAY

12   SUNDAY

GINGER & PEAR PUDDING

225g plain flour
1 tablespoon ground ginger
1 teaspoon ground cinnamon
80g dark brown muscovado sugar
125g golden syrup
125g black treacle
125g unsalted butter, diced
150ml milk
1 teaspoon bicarbonate of soda
5 small pears (see above)
30g walnut pieces
1 medium free-range egg, at room temperature, beaten to mix
icing sugar, for dusting

For the sticky filling and topping
200g dark brown muscovado sugar
100g unsalted butter
150ml double cream
good pinch of sea salt

You will also need
1 x 23cm springclip tin, greased with butter and base-lined

JUNE

13 Tennis competition — MONDAY

14 — TUESDAY

15 — WEDNESDAY

16 — THURSDAY

17 — FRIDAY

18 Dads Highland cross — SATURDAY

19 — SUNDAY

Father's Day

GINGER & PEAR PUDDING

1 Heat your oven to 180°C/350°F/gas 4. Sift the flour, ground ginger, cinnamon and sugar into a mixing bowl. Make a well in the centre.

2 Measure the golden syrup, black treacle and butter into a small pan. Set over low heat and leave to melt gently, stirring now and then. Meanwhile, heat the milk in another small pan until it is warm, but still feels just comfortable when you dip your little finger in. Stir in the bicarbonate of soda and set aside for now. Remove the melted syrup mixture from the heat and leave to cool to lukewarm.

3 While the melted mix is cooling, peel the pears, leaving the stalks attached. Using the tip of a small knife, the end of a peeler or a grapefruit knife, carefully remove the core from each pear, working from the base end. Trim the base so the pear stands upright without wobbling, then stuff the hollow with walnuts (making sure the pear still stands upright).

4 Now make up the sponge mixture. Pour the melted syrup mixture into the well in the flour. Add the just-warm milk mixture and the beaten egg. Working quickly, mix everything together with a whisk or wooden spoon to make a smooth, thick batter. Pour it into the prepared tin.

5 Place the pears in the sponge mix, arranging them so they stand upright, stalks up, and are evenly spaced. Bake in the heated oven for 50–60 minutes until the sponge is risen and firm, and a skewer inserted in the centre comes out clean.

6 Meanwhile, make the sauce. Put the sugar, butter and cream into a medium-sized non-stick saucepan and heat gently until the butter melts. Bring the mixture to the boil, then simmer gently, stirring now and then, for about 5 minutes until thick and toffee-coloured. Remove from the heat, stir in the salt and keep hot.

7 Run a round-bladed knife around the inside of the tin to loosen the sponge, then unclip the side. Serve the pudding warm, dusted with icing sugar and with the sauce. Any leftovers can be eaten like a cake, cut in thick slices.

SERVES SIX

JUNE

20 MONDAY

Longest Day

21 TUESDAY

22 WEDNESDAY

23 THURSDAY

24 FRIDAY

25 SATURDAY

26 SUNDAY

NOTES

JUNE/JULY

27   MONDAY

28   TUESDAY

29   WEDNESDAY

30   THURSDAY

1   FRIDAY

2   SATURDAY

3   SUNDAY

ALMOND, HAZELNUT AND WHITE CHOCOLATE LAYER CAKE

This cake really is a showstopper, with six layers of delicate sponge coated in a white chocolate mousse icing.

JULY

4   MONDAY

5   TUESDAY

6   WEDNESDAY

7   THURSDAY

8   FRIDAY

9   SATURDAY

10   SUNDAY

ALMOND, HAZELNUT AND WHITE CHOCOLATE LAYER CAKE

For the icing

3 leaves of gelatine

700ml double cream

300g white chocolate, broken into pieces

4 tablespoons Frangelico

For the hazelnut sponge

275g unsalted butter, softened

275g caster sugar

5 medium eggs

50g roasted chopped
hazelnuts

250g self-raising flour

50g ground almonds

You will also need

3 X 18cm round, loose-bottomed sandwich tins, buttered and lined

JULY

11 MONDAY

12 TUESDAY

Holiday (Northern Ireland)

13 WEDNESDAY

14 THURSDAY

15 FRIDAY

16 SATURDAY

17 SUNDAY

ALMOND, HAZELNUT AND WHITE CHOCOLATE LAYER CAKE

1 For the icing, soak the gelatine in a bowl of cold water for a couple of minutes. Meanwhile, put 350ml of the cream into a pan. Bring to the boil, then remove from the heat. Remove the gelatine from the water and squeeze out as much excess water as possible. Add to the cream, stirring until dissolved.

2 Put the white chocolate in a food processor and, with the motor running, slowly add the hot cream in a steady stream. Whizz until smooth, then spoon into a bowl, cover with clingfilm and leave to cool. Chill for about 30 minutes.

3 Whisk the remaining cream with the Frangelico to stiff peaks, then fold into the chilled chocolate mixture. Cover with clingfilm and chill for up to 3 hours.

4 Heat the oven to 180°C/350°F/gas 4. Beat the butter and sugar together using a hand-held electric whisk until light and fluffy. Add the eggs, one at a time, beating really well before adding the next.

5 Whizz the hazelnuts in a food processor with 100g of the flour. Fold this and the rest of the flour and the ground almonds into the sponge mixture. Divide between the prepared tins, place in the heated oven and bake for 30 minutes until the sponges are golden and a skewer inserted into the centre comes out clean.

6 Turn out the sponges onto a wire rack and leave to cool. Once cool, slice each in half horizontally to make six layers. Put one sponge base on a serving plate or cake stand. Using a palette knife, spread a layer of the icing, then repeat with the remaining sponge layers. Cover the sides and top of the cake with the icing (working quickly as the icing will soften as you work; if it becomes too soft, chill the icing and the cake for 30 minutes).

SERVES TWELVE

JULY

18   MONDAY

19   TUESDAY

20   WEDNESDAY

21   THURSDAY

22   FRIDAY

23   SATURDAY

24   SUNDAY

NOTES

JULY

25 MONDAY

26 TUESDAY

27 WEDNESDAY

28 THURSDAY

29 FRIDAY

30 SATURDAY

31 SUNDAY

NOTES

AUGUST

1

MONDAY

Holiday (Scotland & Republic of Ireland)

2

TUESDAY

3

WEDNESDAY

4

THURSDAY

5

FRIDAY

6

SATURDAY

7

SUNDAY

SUMMER BERRY & NUT CAKE

Just the cake for a tea party in summer, when British berries taste best and are good value too. The simple sponge has a jammy covering of berries and then a nut topping. The layers bake together to make an exceptional cake – crunchy yet juicy, and buttery!

AUGUST

8 MONDAY

9 TUESDAY

10 WEDNESDAY

11 THURSDAY

12 FRIDAY

13 SATURDAY

14 SUNDAY

SUMMER BERRY & NUT CAKE

For the topping
75g marzipan, diced

25g unsalted butter, chilled and diced

2 tablespoons plain flour

75g light brown muscovado sugar

½ teaspoon ground cinnamon

50g walnut pieces

icing sugar, for dusting

For the berry mix
150g each dessert blackberries, raspberries, blueberries and strawberries

For the sponge mixture
125g unsalted butter, softened

145g caster sugar

2 medium free-range eggs, at room temperature

½ teaspoon vanilla extract

250g plain flour

1½ teaspoons baking powder

¼ teaspoon bicarbonate of soda

½ teaspoon ground cinnamon

125ml buttermilk

50g walnut pieces, chopped smaller

You will also need
1 x 23cm springclip tin, greased with butter and base-lined

AUGUST

15 MONDAY

16 TUESDAY

17 WEDNESDAY

18 THURSDAY

19 FRIDAY

20 SATURDAY

21 SUNDAY

SUMMER BERRY & NUT CAKE

1 Heat your oven to 180°C/350°F/gas 4. To make the topping, put all the ingredients into the bowl of a food processor and run the machine briefly, just until the mixture looks like gravel – stop the machine before the mix starts to come together to form a paste. Set on one side for now.

2 Put the blackberries, raspberries and blueberries into a mixing bowl (if you rinse them first, make sure they are well drained and then dried on kitchen paper to prevent them from becoming soggy). Hull the strawberries and halve any larger ones. Add to the bowl and toss gently just to combine the berries. Put on one side while you make the sponge mixture.

3 Put the soft butter and caster sugar into a mixing bowl (or the bowl of a free-standing electric mixer fitted with the whisk attachment). Beat with a wooden spoon or a hand-held electric mixer (or in the free-standing mixer) until fluffy and light. Scrape down the sides of the bowl. Using a fork beat the eggs with the vanilla extract in a small bowl, just until frothy. Gradually add the egg mixture to the creamed butter mixture, a tablespoon at a time, beating well after each addition. Sift the flour, baking powder, bicarbonate of soda and cinnamon into the bowl. Add the buttermilk and walnuts. Gently but thoroughly fold everything together using a large metal spoon or a plastic spatula. The mixture will be fairly stiff.

4 Spoon into the prepared tin and spread evenly. Scatter the berries on top, distributing them evenly (so each slice of cake has a selection of fruit); avoid mounding them up in the middle as this will slow the rate at which the centre of the cake bakes. Sprinkle the topping mixture over the berries in an even layer.

5 Bake in the heated oven for about 1 ¼ hours until the topping is a good golden brown with the berry juices bubbling up through it. Test to be sure the sponge is cooked by inserting a wooden cocktail stick into the middle – it should come out clean (because of the jammy fruit mixture it's best to test in several spots).

6 Set the cake, in its tin, on a wire rack. Run a round-bladed knife around the inside of the tin to loosen the cake, then leave to cool for 15 minutes before gently unclipping the tin side. Dust the cake with icing sugar and serve slightly warm or at room temperature. Best eaten the same day.

MAKES ONE LARGE CAKE

AUGUST

22   MONDAY

23   TUESDAY

24   WEDNESDAY

25   THURSDAY

26   FRIDAY

27   SATURDAY

28   SUNDAY

NOTES

....
....
....
....
....
....
....
....
....
....
....
....
....
....
....
....
....
....
....
....
....
....
....
....
....

AUGUST/SEPTEMBER

29 MONDAY

Late Summer Holiday (UK)

30 TUESDAY

31 WEDNESDAY

1 THURSDAY

2 FRIDAY

3 SATURDAY

4 SUNDAY

PUMPKIN & SUNFLOWER BISCUITS

Thin, crunchy, round crackers bursting with seeds are served with a chutney of red onions slowly cooked with roasted caraway seeds. Perfect with a good extra mature Cheddar.

SEPTEMBER

5   MONDAY

6   TUESDAY

7   WEDNESDAY

8   THURSDAY

9   FRIDAY

10   SATURDAY

11   SUNDAY

Rememberence day

PUMPKIN & SUNFLOWER BISCUITS

For the biscuits

70g rye flour

70g plain wholemeal flour

120g plain white flour

50g pumpkin seeds

50g sunflower seeds

small bunch of chives, finely chopped (about 5g)

1 teaspoon English mustard powder

1 teaspoon fine salt

1 ½ teaspoons baking powder

30g sun-dried tomato purée

3 tablespoons olive oil

180ml cold water

For the chutney

4 large red onions, thinly sliced

50g caster sugar

½ teaspoon caraway seeds, toasted and ground

50ml red wine vinegar

50ml red wine

1 teaspoon good blackcurrant squash, or to taste

You will also need

1–2 baking sheets, lined with baking paper

7cm plain round cutter

SEPTEMBER

12 MONDAY

13 TUESDAY

14 WEDNESDAY

15 THURSDAY

16 FRIDAY

17 SATURDAY

18 SUNDAY

PUMPKIN & SUNFLOWER BISCUITS

1 To make the dough, put the 3 flours into a mixing bowl and add the next 6 ingredients. Mix well. Make a well in the mixture and add the tomato purée, oil and half the water. Mix these ingredients together, then gradually work in the dry ingredients, using your hand, adding more water as needed to make a soft but not sticky dough (you may not need all the water).

2 Turn out the dough onto a lightly floured worktop and knead for 5 minutes until it feels firmer and very supple. Shape into a ball and cover it with the upturned bowl. Leave to relax for 15 minutes while you heat the oven to 230°C/450°F/gas 8.

3 Divide the dough in half. Keep one portion covered by the upturned bowl, while you roll out the other portion to a very thin rectangle, about 30 x 35cm. Cover the dough rectangle with the sheet of baking paper you are using to line the baking sheet, then roll up the dough (with the paper inside) around the rolling pin. Lift the pin over the baking sheet, then gently unroll the dough – with the paper – onto the baking sheet so the paper is underneath the dough. If necessary, trim off any dough hanging over the edges of the baking sheet.

4 Bake in the heated oven for about 7 minutes until the top of the dough is golden. Remove the baking sheet from the oven and set it on a heatproof surface. Using a large palette knife to help you, flip the dough over, then return to the oven to bake the second side until lightly coloured, about 6 minutes.

5 Slide the sheet of dough onto a large board and quickly stamp out rounds using the cutter. Alternatively, cut the sheet into squares or rectangles using a large, sharp knife. Return the cut biscuits to the lined baking sheet and bake for a further 5 minutes until crisp and golden. Leave to cool on a wire rack while you bake the second batch of biscuits in the same way.

6 While they are cooling, make the chutney. Put the onions, sugar and ground caraway into a medium-sized heavy-based pan. Cover tightly and cook the onions over medium heat, stirring occasionally, for 15 minutes until very soft and tender. Add the vinegar and wine and cook uncovered over medium heat for 10 minutes until very thick. Taste and add squash as needed to flavour the chutney. Leave to cool, then spoon into a bowl or jar. Serve with the biscuits and good strong cheese.

MAKES ABOUT TWENTY-FOUR PLUS A SMALL JAR OF CHUTNEY

SEPTEMBER

19 MONDAY

20 TUESDAY

21 WEDNESDAY

The United Nations International Day of Peace

22 THURSDAY

23 FRIDAY

24 SATURDAY

25 SUNDAY

NOTES

....
....
....
....
....
....
....
....
....
....
....
....
....
....
....
....
....
....
....
....
....
....
....

SEPTEMBER/OCTOBER

26 MONDAY

27 TUESDAY

28 WEDNESDAY

29 THURSDAY

30 FRIDAY

1 SATURDAY

2 SUNDAY

Al Hijra

LINZERTORTE

An Austrian recipe dating back hundreds of years, this latticed bake – a little like a spiced jam tart – has many versions, but all have a nutty, very crumbly base of hazelnuts or almonds with a rich, jammy filling. Redcurrant jam is traditionally used, but as it is hard to find outside Austria, this recipe uses a mixture of redcurrant jelly and raspberry jam.

OCTOBER

3 MONDAY

Rosh Hashanah (Jewish New Year)

4 TUESDAY

5 WEDNESDAY

6 THURSDAY

7 FRIDAY

8 SATURDAY

9 SUNDAY

LINZERTORTE

3 tablespoons dry, fine breadcrumbs
8 tablespoons each of redcurrant jelly and raspberry jam
1 medium egg yolk, beaten with 1 teaspoon water, for glazing

For the crust
150g finely ground hazelnuts (see Tip)
275g plain flour, plus extra for dusting
1 teaspoon ground cinnamon
a pinch of ground cloves
½ teaspoon salt
225g cold unsalted butter, cut into cubes
85g icing sugar
2 medium egg yolks
finely grated zest of 1 lemon and a squeeze of juice

You will also need
30 x 20cm fluted, rectangular, Loose-bottomed tart tin, greased

OCTOBER

10 MONDAY

11 TUESDAY

12 WEDNESDAY

Yom Kippur (Day of Atonement)

13 THURSDAY

14 FRIDAY

15 SATURDAY

16 SUNDAY

LINZERTORTE

1 To make the crust, mix the ground hazelnuts, flour, ground spices and salt in a bowl. Add the butter and, with your fingertips, rub into the flour mixture until it resembles breadcrumbs. Add the icing sugar, stir well, then quickly mix in the egg yolks, lemon zest and a squeeze of juice so it starts to come together.

2 Turn out onto a lightly floured surface and knead briefly until smooth. Remove one-third of the dough. Shape the smaller piece into a disc, wrap in clingfilm and chill in the fridge for 10 minutes. Meanwhile, heat the oven to 180°C/350°F/gas 4.

3 Roll out the remaining dough on a lightly floured surface into a rectangle large enough to line the tart tin. Lift into the tin and press into an even layer over the base and sides, patching any gaps, as the dough is very crumbly. Add any trimmings to the pastry disc in the fridge. Chill the base for 10 minutes.

4 Place the base in the heated oven and bake for 10–15 minutes until it has barely begun to colour, then set aside to cool. While the base is baking, roll out the remaining dough between 2 sheets of non-stick baking paper into a rectangle about 32 x 22cm, then return to the fridge and chill for 20 minutes.

5 Sprinkle the cooked base of the torte with the breadcrumbs, then spoon the redcurrant jelly and raspberry jam evenly over the top (spoon on in blobs and then use a palette knife to spread them out).

6 Remove the chilled pastry from the fridge and take off the sheets of baking paper. Cut the pastry into strips, about 1.5cm wide, across the diagonal (if you have a fluted pastry wheel you can create a lovely crimped edge to your strips). Lay these one at a time over the jam, using a long spatula as the pastry is crumbly, to make a criss-cross lattice pattern. Neaten any excess pastry at the edges by pressing it against the side of the tin.

7 Brush the pastry with the egg glaze, put in the heated oven and bake for 45–50 minutes until golden all over. Allow to cool for 10 minutes before removing from the tin. Cut into portions and serve.

TIP
To grind hazelnuts without them turning oily, place them in a food processor with half of the flour and pulse together until the hazelnuts are finely ground into the flour. If you want you can continue to make the pastry in the food processor.

SERVES TEN

OCTOBER

17   MONDAY

18   TUESDAY

19   WEDNESDAY

20   THURSDAY

21   FRIDAY

22   SATURDAY

23   SUNDAY

NOTES

....
....
....
....
....
....
....
....
....
....
....
....
....
....
....
....
....
....
....
....
....
....
....
....
....
....

OCTOBER

24

25

26

27

28

29

30

Daylight Saving Ends / Diwali

NOTES

....
....
....
....
....
....
....
....
....
....
....
....
....
....
....
....
....
....
....
....
....

OCTOBER/NOVEMBER

31 MONDAY

Emma's birthday

Holiday (Republic of Ireland) / Halloween

1 TUESDAY

2 WEDNESDAY

3 THURSDAY

4 FRIDAY

5 SATURDAY

Guy Fawkes Night

6 SUNDAY

TRIFLE WITH HOMEMADE MADEIRA CAKE

A true British classic, this overly large bowl of beautifully layered boozy trifle is a winner. The homemade Madeira cake is well worth the extra effort.

NOVEMBER

7 .... MONDAY

8 .... TUESDAY

9 .... WEDNESDAY

10 .... THURSDAY

11 .... FRIDAY

12 .... SATURDAY

13 .... SUNDAY

Remembrance Sunday

TRIFLE WITH HOMEMADE MADEIRA CAKE

125ml Madeira or sweet sherry

450ml double cream

2 tablespoons icing sugar

2 tablespoons brandy

For the poached pears

5 firm, ripe pears, peeled

pared zest of 1 lemon

1 cinnamon stick, snapped in half

4 cloves

200g caster sugar

1 bottle full-bodied red wine

For the cake

175g unsalted butter

175g caster sugar

finely grated zest of 1 lemon

½ teaspoon vanilla extract

3 large eggs

200g self-raising flour

50g ground almonds

For the custard

350ml double cream

350ml full-fat milk

1 vanilla pod, slit in half lengthways and seeds scraped

4 medium egg yolks

2 tablespoons cornflour

75g caster sugar

2 leaves of gelatine

You will also need

900g loaf tin, greased and lined

2.5 litre trifle bowl

NOVEMBER

14   MONDAY

15   TUESDAY

16   WEDNESDAY

17   THURSDAY

18   FRIDAY

19   SATURDAY

20   SUNDAY

TRIFLE WITH HOMEMADE MADEIRA CAKE

1 Put the pears in a pan with the pared zest, cinnamon, cloves, sugar and wine. Bring to a simmer and cook very gently for 15-20 minutes until tender to the point of a knife. Leave to cool in the liquid.

2 To make the cake, heat the oven to 180°C/350°F/gas 4. Whisk the butter with the sugar using a hand-held electric whisk until light and fluffy, then add the lemon zest and vanilla. Gradually beat in the eggs, one at a time, whisking well between each addition. Fold in the flour and ground almonds and spoon into the prepared loaf tin, smoothing the top.

3 Place the cake in the heated oven and bake for 40-50 minutes or until a skewer inserted into the centre comes out clean. Leave to cool in the tin for 10 minutes then turn out onto a wire rack and leave to cool completely.

4 Meanwhile, to make the custard, put the cream and milk into a heavy-based saucepan and add the vanilla seeds and pod. Whisk together the egg yolks, cornflour and sugar in a bowl. Soak the gelatine in a small bowl of cold water. Bring the cream mixture to a gentle simmer, then pour, with the vanilla pod, onto the egg mixture, whisking constantly to prevent curdling. Return to the cleaned-out pan and stir over a low heat until the mixture thickens – it should thickly coat the back of a spoon – and spoon into a bowl. Squeeze the water from the gelatine, add it to the custard and stir to dissolve. Cover the surface with clingfilm to stop a skin forming. Leave to cool completely.

5 Once the cake is cold, cut it into 5cm cubes (if you have a little too much for your bowl, keep the rest for eating with a cup of tea) and arrange in the bottom of the trifle bowl, then sprinkle with the Madeira or sherry. Slice the poached pears into halves, remove the cores, and arrange on top of the cake in the bowl.

6 Remove the vanilla pod from the cooled custard and dollop the custard all over the fruit, then put in the fridge to firm up fully for an hour or so. When ready to serve, whisk the cream, icing sugar and brandy together until it forms soft peaks. Spoon it over the custard and serve immediately.

THINKING AHEAD
Start your trifle well in advance. You can make the cake and poach the pears the day before, then make the custard and assemble the trifle on the day itself.

SERVES EIGHT

NOVEMBER

21   MONDAY

22   TUESDAY

23   WEDNESDAY

24   THURSDAY

25   FRIDAY

26   SATURDAY

27   SUNDAY

NOTES

NOVEMBER/DECEMBER

28 MONDAY

29 TUESDAY

30 WEDNESDAY

St. Andrew's Day (Scotland)

1 THURSDAY

Rachels birthday

2 FRIDAY

3 SATURDAY

Katies birthday

4 SUNDAY

CINNAMON AND RASPBERRY WHIRL WREATH

This delicious wreath is made from a sweet, enriched dough coated in fruity jam. It emerges from the oven with the aroma of freshly baked bread and yuletide spirit. Once cool, adorn your wreath with a festive ribbon and eat within 3 days.

DECEMBER

5   MONDAY

6   TUESDAY

7   WEDNESDAY

8   THURSDAY

9   FRIDAY

10   SATURDAY

11   SUNDAY

CINNAMON AND RASPBERRY WHIRL WREATH

350ml full-fat milk

60g caster sugar

10 cardamom pods, crushed

85g unsalted butter

1 x 7g sachet fast-action dried yeast

1 medium egg

500g plain flour, plus extra for dusting

1 teaspoon salt

For the filling

4 tablespoons raspberry jam

2 teaspoons ground cinnamon, mixed
with 2 teaspoons caster sugar

DECEMBER

12   MONDAY

13   TUESDAY

14   WEDNESDAY

15   THURSDAY

16   FRIDAY

17   SATURDAY

18   SUNDAY

CINNAMON AND RASPBERRY WHIRL WREATH

1 Warm the milk in a pan with the sugar and cardamom. Once steaming, add the butter and let it melt, then remove from the heat and leave to infuse for 4-5 minutes. Pour through a sieve into a jug, cool until only just warm, then add the yeast and egg and mix well.

2 Sift the flour into a large bowl with the salt and make a well in the centre. Add the liquid and mix with your hands until it all comes together. If it is a little too dry add a splash more milk, and if it feels a little too wet you can add a little more flour, but err on the wetter side to avoid a dry dough.

3 Turn out onto a lightly floured work surface and knead for 5-10 minutes until smooth and elastic. Return to the clean bowl, cover with a clean tea towel and leave in a warm place for about 1 hour or until doubled in size.

4 Punch down the dough with your knuckles and turn out onto a lightly floured surface. Roll it out to a rectangle about 25 x 45cm, with the long side towards you. Spread the jam evenly over the dough and sprinkle with the cinnamon mixture, leaving a 2cm border on the long side closest to you.

5 Roll the dough up as tightly as you can, starting from the long side furthest from you. Slice the dough in half along its length to expose the layers. Starting at one end, cross the pieces over each other, keeping the exposed layers uppermost, working down the length of the dough, then transfer to a lined baking sheet and shape into a wreath by folding the four ends over each other to continue the plait.

6 Cover with a clean tea towel or lightly greased clingfilm and leave in a warm place for 1 hour, or until doubled in size. Meanwhile, heat the oven to 180°C/350°F/gas 4.

7 Place the wreath in the heated oven and bake for 30-35 minutes until lightly golden, then remove from the oven and transfer to a wire rack to cool before serving.

> **TIP**
> If your kitchen is a little cold, heat your oven to 50°C/120°F/lowest gas setting, then turn it off. Place the bowl of dough in the warm, but switched off, oven to prove.

THINKING AHEAD
Freeze the proved, unbaked wreath on a baking sheet until solid, then wrap well in baking paper and foil or clingfilm and freeze for up to 3 months. Defrost fully before baking.

MAKES ONE LARGE WREATH

DECEMBER

19 MONDAY

Trip out

20 TUESDAY

Christmas dance

21 WEDNESDAY

Choir performance

22 THURSDAY

Xmas dinner at School

23 FRIDAY

Dentist
Choir Performance

24 SATURDAY

Christmas Eve

25 SUNDAY

Christmas!!!

Merry christmac

DECEMBER

26 MONDAY

Boxing Day / St. Stephen's Day (Republic of Ireland)

27 TUESDAY

Christmas Bank Holiday

28 WEDNESDAY

29 THURSDAY

30 FRIDAY

31 SATURDAY

New Year's Eve

1 SUNDAY

NOTES

NOTES

NOTES

NOTES

NOTES

NOTES

NOTES

NOTES